Northamptonshire
County Council
Libraries and Information

C000162035

COPING SUCCESSFULLY WITH YOUR HYPERACTIVE CHILD

DR PAUL CARSON, B.A., M.B., B.Ch., B.A.O., D.F.P.A., holds an Asthma and Allergy Clinic as part of his private practice in Dublin, and has helped many hyperactive children. He graduated from Trinity College, Dublin, in 1975 and spent six years working in Australia and England before returning to Ireland. He is a regular contributor to the *Irish Medical Times, Woman's Way, U-Magazine* and the Healthfax Press Agency in London, and he is the author of *How to Cope with Your Child's Allergies* (Sheldon Press). In addition to writing, he lectures regularly to both doctors and the general public on asthma and allergic conditions.

Sarah Nichols is the mother of a hyperactive child and co-ordinates the Hyperactive Child Support Groups in Ireland.

Overcoming Common Problems Series

The ABC of Eating
Coping with anorexia, bulimia and
compulsive eating
JOY MELVILLE

Acne
How it's caused and how to cure it
PAUL VAN RIEL

An A–Z of Alternative Medicine
BRENT Q. HAFEN AND KATHRYN J.
FRANDSEN

Arthritis
Is your suffering really necessary?
DR WILLIAM FOX

Birth Over Thirty
SHEILA KITZINGER

Body Language
How to read others' thoughts by their gestures
ALLAN PEASE

Calm Down
How to cope with frustration and anger
DR PAUL HAUCK

Common Childhood Illnesses
DR PATRICIA GILBERT

Coping with Depression and Elation
DR PATRICK McKEON

Curing Arthritis Cookbook
MARGARET HILLS

Curing Arthritis – The Drug-free Way
MARGARET HILLS

Depression
DR PAUL HAUCK

Divorce and Separation
ANGELA WILLANS

Enjoying Motherhood
DR BRUCE PITT

The Epilepsy Handbook
SHELAGH McGOVERN

Everything You Need to Know about Contact Lenses
DR ROBERT YOUNGSON

Everything You Need to Know about Your Eyes
DR ROBERT YOUNGSON

Everything You Need to Know about Shingles
DR ROBERT YOUNGSON

Family First Aid and Emergency Handbook
DR ANDREW STANWAY

Fears and Phobias
What they are and how to overcome them
DR TONY WHITEHEAD

Feverfew
A traditional herbal remedy for migraine and arthritis
DR STEWART JOHNSON

Fight Your Phobia and Win
DAVID LEWIS

Fit Kit
DAVID LEWIS

Flying Without Fear
TESSA DUCKWORTH AND DAVID MILLER

Goodbye Backache
DR DAVID IMRIE WITH COLLEEN DIMSON

Guilt
Why it happens and how to overcome it
DR VERNON COLEMAN

How to Bring Up your Child Successfully
DR PAUL HAUCK

How to Control your Drinking
DRS W. MILLER AND R. MUNOZ

How to Cope with Stress
DR PETER TYRER

Overcoming Common Problems Series

Overcoming Common Problems Series

Overcoming Common Problems

COPING SUCCESSFULLY
WITH YOUR
HYPERACTIVE CHILD

Dr Paul Carson

B.A., M.B., B.Ch., B.A.O., D.F.P.A.

SHELDON PRESS
LONDON

First published in Great Britain by
Sheldon Press, SPCK, Marylebone Road, London NW1 4DU

Copyright © Dr Paul J. Carson 1987

British Library Cataloguing in Publication Data

Carson, Paul
   How to cope successfully with your
   hyperactive child. ———(Overcoming common
   problems)
   1. Hyperactive children
   I. Title II. Series
   618.92'8589   RJ506.H9

   ISBN 0–85969–543–3
   ISBN 0–85969–544–1 Pbk

Filmset by Deltatype, Ellesmere Port

Printed in Great Britain by
Richard Clay Ltd, Bungay, Suffolk

Contents

To the children
of Gawler and Munno Para, South Australia

Foreword

Both parents looked as if they were at their wits' end and readily confessed to feeling that way. The mother was pale and haggard, distraught with worry; the father tired, drawn and more than a little edgy as the consultation progressed. The reason for their physical and mental condition was out in the waiting room producing similar feelings in my receptionist. He was only four years old but caused more chaos in a few minutes than a bus load of kids! He stayed with us for an hour and that was as much as we could take — his unfortunate parents had him all day, every day. Over the years they had tried every possible approach towards management and met with little success. They were desperate, disillusioned and exhausted.

After reading an article in a newspaper about hyperactive children they quickly concluded their little boy's behaviour fitted this description. Hence the approach to me — would a special diet help their child?

Hyperactivity in children is a poorly defined, hotly disputed condition which is more common than most doctors imagine or accept. The hyperactive child is like a scaled down King Kong, causing disruption, distress and chaos wherever he goes. The behavioural pattern is extreme and incessant, often causing equally extreme responses from parents and relatives. Many of these children are labelled 'spoiled brats', and their parents blamed for their mismanagement. They in turn become confused and desperate, unsure of where to go for help or what to do next. Marriages are put under immense strain and relationships crumble as the pressure is kept up from the child's behaviour.

In this book I will discuss the features of some aberrant behaviour patterns in children and explain possible causes. I will set out guidelines for a diagnosis of the true hyper-active child so that you can determine whether your own child's behaviour fits this category. In addition I will review the link between diet and behaviour in children. By the time you have read the book through you will have a clearer understanding of what is (and is not) hyperactive behaviour and how it can be managed. Using the guidelines I suggest you will avoid the confusion and frustration of the many ridiculous theories and practices associated with this con-dition, and go straight to the correct diagnosis and manage-ment routine.

1

Hyperactivity — A Review of the Condition

For many years doctors and other health professionals have been aware of hyperactivity, a bizarre form of extreme behaviour in children that has proved difficult both to investigate and to manage successfully. Many theories have been put forward to explain why children are affected but none has been really satisfactory to either parents or doctors. Indeed most of the suggestions have not stood up to detailed crtical examination.

Brain damage at birth was one hypothesis that was quite acceptable for a number of years. This was despite the fact that in almost all these children no objective evidence of brain damage could be found. 'Miminal brain damage' became the label that let many a doctor off the hook when searching desperately for an explanation for yet another child's overactive pattern. The 'minimal' part was an inspired addition — it meant that the amount of brain damage was just enough to produce the aberrant behaviour but not enough to show on brain scanning. A perfect label, in a fact, as parents couldn't get around the diagnosis, no matter how dissatisfied they might be with the explanation. A variety of treatments and behaviour-modification programmes were tried with varying degrees of success. Amphetamines — drugs which stimulate the brain — were (and still are) prescribed and indeed did produce an improvement in certain children. Phenobarbitones (barbiturates — drugs which depress the brain activity and cause sedation) actually made the situation worse.

The condition was researched in depth in the United States and here the long-term follow-up studies confirmed what most parents feared: hyperactive children had persisting problems in academic attainment, social adaptation and emotional development. Their impulsive behavioural characteristic persisted into adulthood with often disastrous results. Despite reassurances that their hyperactive child would 'grow out of' the behaviour pattern, most did not and continued to be disruptive for years.

In 1915, when the child-guidance movement began in the United Sates, there was still little attention paid to the learning-impaired and misbehaving child. In the 1920s and 1930s children with major behaviour problems were seen by psychiatrists and often referred to social workers and social agencies. Any attempt at treatment was directed towards psychoanalysis. From the 1930s to the 1950s the American middle and upper classes developed in strength and expressed concern about the education and development of children. At this time mental health professionals dealing with those children (whom we might now recognize as hyperactive) concentrated on family and group therapies, drug treatment, residential care and remedial education. By the late 1960s, spurred on by the successes of drug therapy in other areas of psychiatry, hyperactive children were increasingly treated with medication, particularly amphetamines. In the 1970s there was a public commitment to aid all disadvantaged children — the battered child, the malnourished child, the slow learner, etc. But, over a 50-year period in the United States alone, as psychiatry improved and successes in treatments were claimed, one condition remained stubbornly resistant to management — the hyperactive child.

In 1973, Dr Ben Feingold, an allergist working in California, suggested that certain foods and artificial colourings and flavourings were a cause of hyperactivity. Dr Feingold proposed a diet free from these substances as both treatment and preventative of the condition. He published two popular books on the subject, *Why Your Child is Hyperactive* (1974) and *The Feingold Cookbook for Hyperactive Children* (1979). Many parents adopted his diet for their hyperactive children and some reported a noticeable improvement.

In later publications, Feingold revised his recommendations, concentrating more on artificial food additives and less on troublesome foods (called 'salicylate foods' because they contained a natural amount of substances known as salicylates).

Adherence to the Fiengold diet, sometimes referred to as the KP diet (after the Kaiser Permanente Clinic where Feingold worked), involved the elimination of most fruits and many vegetables, at least for the first weeks. Almost all manufactured foods were also eliminated, as were tea, coffee, margarine, coloured butter and condiments. These restrictions made it almost impossible to eat in a school cafeteria or restaurant. Many non-food items such as mouthwashes, toothpastes, cough drops, perfumes and certain medicines were also prohibited. To prevent the child becoming isolated with the diet and to reduce the temptation to break the routine, Feingold encouraged the whole family to participate. This had the added advantage of team involvement and a group goal. Feingold reported that 40–70 per cent of the hyperactive children who adhered strictly to his diet demonstrated a marked reduction in hyperactive behaviour. Of those who responded to treatment, two-thirds did so dramatically, an effect especially marked among the younger children.

Feingold produced a major split in the management of hyperactivity — parents took to his theory and diet with enthusiasm and became strong supporters. Doctors and other health professionals were suspicious and often openly hostile. Many dismissed as nonsense his observation that hyperactive children did respond to the KP diet.

The apparent non-acceptance by doctors of the diet–behaviour link in hyperactivity has been a source of division and subsequent confusion among those people seeking to help the children involved. It has also been the spur towards the formation of a branch of the Hyperactive Child Support Group in many countries. This is a self-help group of concerned families who are united by their common problem — hyperactivity in one (or more) of their children. The Hyperactive

Child Support Group has grown very quickly and has thriving local branches in almost every area of Britain, Ireland, Australia, New Zealand — in fact every country where the problem exists.

At public meetings held by the Hyperactive Child Support Group, parents sometimes complain bitterly about the attitude of the medical profession to hyperactivity. Indeed the complaints often border on downright hostility. Families relate how they have been bounced from pillar to post among various health professionals, frequently receiving confusing and contradictory advice. More than a few recall the open criticism they have experienced of their management of the child involved, leading to an undermining of confidence and feelings of inadequacy. If they asked about the possibility of a special diet to help the situation the chances were they would get a derisory reply. By the time they had heard of and finally made contact with the Hyperactive Child Support Group, they were disillusioned, distressed and desperate for help.

At the Hyperactive Child Support Group they receive sympathy, helpful suggestions and, above all, hope. They also learn how many other families have had similar experiences, and, as 'horror stories' are swopped, a genuine bitterness sets in. If, as very often happens, the advice from the group turns out to be of more help than that offered before, the dissatisfaction with doctors becomes total. 'Why did we have to go through so much misery before finding the solution for ourselves?' is a common gut reaction at this stage. As others relate similar feelings of distress the conclusion is soon reached that most doctors are ignorant, uncaring and unsympathetic of the hyperactive child problem. Nothing could be further from the truth.

In Great Britain and Ireland the medical profession tends to be a conservative group, especially when compared to some of their colleagues in the United States. However, a conservative doctor is not a bad doctor, or a doctor with a closed mind. Indeed the natural reluctance to jump at every new theory or treatment is in everyone's interest. Many a weird and wonderful idea has been touted over the years as a miracle cure for every ailment under the sun and doctors have had to keep a sense of proportion when assessing these claims and their proponents. For as long as there is still ill-health there will always be 'chancers' out to exploit the vulnerability of the sufferer and make a profit

Where hyperactivity is concerned, the treatment choices are often so severe that any alternatives are likely to be tried in preference. This is what happened when Dr Ben Feingold suggested the link between diet and hyperactivity — parents were very keen to give his treatment a chance but the medical profession didn't show the same enthusiasm.

Over subsequent years the split widened, particularly as the proponents of the dietary treatment often included 'fringe' practitioners, whose ideas on a wide range of medical problems were not altogether orthodox or immediately sensible.

In fairness to doctors, their reluctance to take Feingold's diet seriously was based on sound evidence. Whenever his theory was put to the test the results did not reflect the claims he was making. Repeated studies of hyperactive behaviour patterns in children when given a trial of the Feingold diet came to the same conclusion: some children did exhibit markedly better behaviour when on the diet, but not enough to be significant. As many as seven different trials were performed in different centres throughout the world to test the Feingold hypothesis — the results were more or less the same at the end of each study. With these results consistently the same over the years, what conclusion could doctors come to other than what they could see with their own eyes — the Feingold diet and theory had no part to play in the management of hyperactive children? A nice try, admittedly, and great if it had proved true, but nevertheless of no practical use.

As you will read later in this book, recent studies have thrown new light on the dietary link and also explain why the Feingold diet did not work for every child. Feingold had the right ideas, but not the complete picture. It appears that many foods, other than what he originally believed, are involved in producing the aberrant behavioural pattern in children. As long as they were included in the treatment diets of the various studies, there would always be indifferent results and little chance of the theory being proven correct.

My own introduction to the dietary link in hyperactivity came in 1981, while working in Australia. At that time I had developed an interest in dealing with children with asthma and one boy that I looked after, called Matthew, also had a moderate form of overactivity. He was by no means the most overactive child I have ever seen but was sufficiently so to keep his parents on their toes. Coupled with his chest condition, the behaviour problem meant that his mother and father were constantly worried about him.

During one consultation his mother queried the link between Matthew's diet and his general ill-health. I gave her a rather testy reply — 'Absolute nonsense; there's no evidence to link these problems at all with food!' She had read an article in a newspaper about diet and hyperactivity and produced it for me. I gave it no more than a cursory glance before returning it with a curt comment about wasting her time and my patience with such ideas.

I didn't see Matthew for some time after that but as the practice was always very busy, this did not register. However, about three months later he was back in again and looking remarkably well. For the first time ever he wasn't clutching a can of Coke or some other soft drink. He seemed remarkably calm and not as fidgety as usual. Even without examining him I could see that his asthma was under control. I made a mental note to congratulate myself!

After examining Matthew I began to discuss how effective his treatment was and commented on his obvious good health. His mother heard me through patiently and then gently informed me that the boy hadn't been on any medication for two months and that the improvement in his condition only came about when his diet had been dramatically altered. The first food to go was milk (and all milk products) followed by unnecessary artificial colourings and preservatives. All sugary products were also forbidden. I listened in stunned silence. First Matthew's sleep pattern improved — he had always been a light, restless sleeper; then his blocked, runny nose and wheezy chest. Within two weeks of being on the diet, his overactive behaviour and marked thirst were noticeably better. By the time he was six weeks into the diet the overall improvement was outstanding. The boy's mother then made a comment I have heard so often since when dealing with similar problems through diet: 'It's as if I only met the real Matthew for the first time recently.' She was quite correct — the child I saw that day was altogether different from the one I had known previously.

From that day on I have taken a lot more notice of what parents say to me when dealing with their children's ill-health. Before this I had, like many other doctors, believed in the traditional medical school teaching: 'Parents are too emotionally involved in their children's situation to be able to give objective opinions.' How wrong such beliefs are should be self-evident, but old attitudes remain stubbornly fixed with some doctors. However, Matthew's story reflects how one doctor's attitude to diet and ill-health was turned upside down in the space of a few minutes. How many other doctors were (and perhaps still are) equally suspicious of the importance of diet is hard to tell. It does seem, when one listens in on Hyperactive Child Group meetings, that the profession still finds it very hard to accept these suggestions. Perhaps this book will go some way towards redressing the balance.

2
The Hyperactive Child —
Features of the Condition

The hyperactive child usually has fair skin, blue eyes and blond or red hair. He is usually male although about a sixth of cases are female. He may be left handed, have a finicky appetite and a marked thirst. While these features seem to be the most common associated with the condition there will always be exceptions who have say, dark hair, brown eyes and are right handed. It is important to recognize that there is a very wide spectrum of normal behaviour in children. An exuberant and active child who plays and lives to the full should not be confused with the disorganized and disruptive hyperactive child whose activities show no set pattern. The normal but energetic child will be happy and interested in play time whereas the hyperactive child will lose interest quickly and move on to a new activity almost at random. He never seems truly at peace with himself or his friends.

There are important, easily identifiable characteristics which I shall now list as major and minor. The major features are the hallmarks of the activity of the of hyperactive child whereas the minor features are less common. In addition I have devised a symptom score card where the features of the condition are listed and which will enable you to make a fairly quick and accurate assessment of your child.

Major Features

Inattentiveness

The child is unable to remain attentive to any one subject or game. He will lose interest quickly and switch attention to another activity in minutes. Parents often report that their child will not (or cannot) listen to stories without his attention wandering constantly.

Overactivity

The child exhibits disorganized, restless, ceaseless activity. He constantly fidgets, is always on the go but rarely does anything constructive. The restless behaviour is noticeable day and night — the child is often a poor, fitful sleeper.

Behavioural problems

The child disturbs other children at school and at play. He repeatedly disrupts games or other organized activities. He frequently speaks out of turn and quite often spontaneously in the middle of other conversations. He may make disruptive noises such as humming, clicking of fingers, and so on. He is often belligerent and involved in minor fights at school. He is frequently very disobedient. (As you can well imagine from this list alone the child is none too popular either!)

Learning impediment

As many as 50 per cent of hyperactive children are poor learners and noticeably lag behind their peers in academic performance. The child may have difficulty retaining spoken words or in distinguishing individual written words. He may have difficulty pronouncing letters, while still able to identify them. His spelling is poor. He can perform addition and subtraction fairly well on the fingers but poorly with pencil and paper. He may appear to have difficulty taking in and applying new information. He may be dyslexic and reverse individual letters when writing.

Immaturity

The psychological and emotional development of the hyperactive child lags behind that of his peers. He is immature. This is reflected in his wishes, his choice of younger friends, his interests and his inability to cope with certain situations. He cries easily, persists longer with 'baby-talk', and is easily frightened. (By the time they reach their teens as many as 70 per cent of hyperactive children are still characterized by their parents as immature.)

Minor Features

Impulsiveness

Without thinking of the consequences, the child will dart from one place to the next. This can often be dangerous, as the child may rush onto busy roads without looking to see if the path is clear.

Peer difficulties

Because of a combination of the features already mentioned, many hyperactive children have great difficulty relating well to their peers.

Low self-esteem

Again because of his behaviour and the reaction of other people, particularly other children, hyperactive children soon discover they are not very popular. This in turn leads to a feeling of low self-esteem. Some children actually react against this by exaggerating their misbehaviour.

Unhappy personality

This is particularly true of the markedly hyperactive child. Parents consistently comment how terribly unhappy they felt their child was throughout the disruptive years.

Associated Physical Features

There are a number of physical characteristics that show quite often in children with overactivity, though it must be said that these characteristics are by no means essential for diagnosis.

These characteristics are: headaches; fits; tummy pains; diarrhoea, flatulence; chronic rhinitis (i.e. blocked runny nose); limb pains; eczema and other skin rashes; mouth ulcers; asthma; hay fever; allergic conjunctivitis (i.e. red itchy watery eyes); intense thirst; and poor, fitful sleep pattern. As you will read in Chapters 3 and 4, many of these are *also* found in some medical conditions or may be the result of certain drug-treatment routines. Indeed it is important to stress that, just because your child has one of these physical characteristics, say, a disturbed sleep pattern, he will not necessarily be hyperactive — unnecessary attention can often be paid to the hyperactive behaviour pattern at the expense of an associated, causative, medical problem.

Symptom Score Card

The questionnaire on page 12 is based on an observation of the features we have described as occurring in the hyperactive child. It will enable you to diagnose your child quickly and with a high degree of accuracy.

Hyperactivity in Children

A score card for presumptive diagnosis

Answer YES if the following accurately describe your child:

1.	Restless, always 'on the go'	YES/NO
2.	Fidgets almost all the time	YES/NO
3.	Easily distracted	YES/NO
4.	Easily frustrated	YES/NO
5.	Demanding of time and attention	YES/NO
6.	Short attention span	YES/NO
7.	Disrupts/disturbs other children	YES/NO
8.	Behavioural pattern unpredictable	YES/NO
9.	Excitable, impulsive	YES/NO
10.	Frequent, unpredictable, often inappropriate mood changes	YES/NO
11.	Often 'glassy eyed'	YES/NO
12.	More than usually thirsty	YES/NO

Score two points for each YES, none for each NO.

A score of

0–6 points indicates your child is unlikely to be hyperactive.

6–20 points indicates that hyperactivity is possible, and that it would be well worthwhile having the child assessed.

20–24 points indicates that your child is almost certainly hyperactive and should be assessed without delay.

Three Case Histories

Let us look at the practical side of this system as applied to some rather different children whose parents suspected they might be hyperactive.

Peter

Peter B. was aged five years and was so overactive and disruptive that I could not examine or assess him properly when he came for evaluation with his parents. He broke two glasses in the space of thirty minutes and distributed my patient information sheets to every nook and cranny of the office! He was a classical hyperactive. His mother remembered him as very active *in utero* and after he was born he cried for the first six months. He appeared colicky and had to be carried around almost all the time. He often moaned in his cot and used to rock to and fro as if in pain. As he grew older the other disruptive features of overactivity became more pronounced.

He was an unhappy boy, always whimpering and screaming for the slightest reason. He was intensely thirsty and drank bottles of orange squash daily. Despite the thirst his appetite was poor and at the age of three years he developed asthma. This was no real surprise, as Peter had been 'chesty' almost from birth. His coughing episodes used to leave him exhausted. Peter's behaviour ruined his parents' lives — they could not go out because no babysitter would mind him and he was no joy to care for even though he was an only child. During the discussion that followed his father openly admitted to hating the child.

Because of his extreme behaviour we elected to diagnose him on the basis of the Symptom Score Card. Peter reached the maximum score of 24 and as his story was so suggestive of a food-related problem I elected to treat him in a three stage programme.

The first step was to eliminate all milk and milk products from his diet. This was because Peter's infancy was marked by a number of problems which were very suggestive of a milk

13

allergy. These included colic, "chestiness", restlessness, and rocking to and fro in his cot (there is a more detailed explanation of the features of milk allergy in infants in Chapter 4). In addition I recommended the removal of all unnecessary artificial colourings and preservatives, as these have been shown conclusively to be a cause of overactivity. Peter's diet prior to this programme was unfortunately quite high in these additives in the form of fizzy drinks, sweets and junk foods — all given to try and placate his moods but serving only to make the situation worse! This routine continued for six weeks and produced a marked improvement in his behaviour allowing us to proceed to the second stage of treatment.

The second step involved a thorough examination and identification of other physical problems. Peter's asthma was not very well controlled and there were other problem foods which I felt he should cut down on. These are the so called 'salicylate' foods (because they have a naturally occurring high content of a chemical called sodium salicylate). I prescribed a special spray inhaler for his chest and asked his mother to restrict the amount of honey, grapes and tea Peter consumed. (This is also explained in detail in Chapter 4.) This stage of his management continued for another six weeks and we saw further improvements.

Peter's behaviour by now was excellent with only the occasional out-bursts related to breaking the diet. The third and final stage of his treatment involved the introduction of a capsule called Evening Primrose Oil. This is a herbal product rich in essential fatty acids and very useful in certain types of hyperactivity. I recommended that Peter start on this as he was still thirsty, although not as much as before. For reasons which are not completely understood the use of Evening Primrose Oil is helpful in those hyperactive children who have a marked thirst as part of their problem. (For further details of Evening Primrose Oil see Chapter 4.)

One year on Peter is a normal, well-adjusted child, loved by father and mother and rediscovered by his friends and relatives.

He no longer requires Evening Primrose Oil but does need the occasional treatment for his asthma. The restricted diet has been relaxed somewhat to allow reduced quantities of the suspect foods but he still reacts to milk, chocolate and certain artificial colourings. It is interesting to note that if he 'binges' on certain foods he becomes irritable and cross whereas he can tolerate small quantities. This is explained in Chapter 4 but it is worth noting at this point that there may be a threshold of tolerance to certain foods which, if exceeded, produces symptoms.

Lynn

In contrast to Peter, Lynn was not so dramatically or obviously hyperactive. She was described as a sullen, moody, unhappy little girl. When I first saw her she was aged four and refused to be examined in any way. Her elder sister had asthma which was identified as allergic in nature. Lynn was forever squabbling with her friends, sister and parents. She was disruptive, inattentive and impulsive. She complained a lot of pains in the head, tummy and limbs but no obvious cause had ever been identified. She was a restless sleeper, a poor eater and always very thirsty. She craved sugar and was forever in trouble because of the many ways she managed to get hold of forbidden sweets. Her behaviour was difficult but not impossible, and not until her sister's asthma cleared when she was taken off all milk produce did her parents really consider the possibility of a dietary cause for her behaviour. The rather dramatic way in which her sister's health recovered on the diet was the spur to have Lynn assessed. But Lynn would not co-operate!

Again we decided to diagnose her on the basis of the Symptom Score Card. Lynn's parents took it home and returned it with 'yes' answers to questions 2,3,4,6,7,10,11 and 12, giving Lynn a total score of 16 which put her into the 'hyperactive until proven otherwise' category.

I suggested a two stage management programme for the child. First all milk and milk products were to be removed from the diet. There were three reasons for this. First, as her older sister had responded so well to a similar diet there was a strong possibility that Lynn might also have a milk intolerance problem. Second, her weaning pattern as a child showed many of the features of cow's milk intolerance. Third, the headaches, tummy pains and limb pains were very suggestive of a food allergy and milk is the main culprit in most children.

The second stage involved a total ban on unnecessary sweet foods. This meant no sweets, chocolates, and fizzy drinks or between meal snacks. In addition certain artificial colourings and preservatives were eliminated.

Lynn's parents went through hell for the first ten days of this dietary regime. The child became intolerable, got up to all sorts of tricks to get sweets and was so anti-social that she was sent home from school! On days 11,12 and 13 her mood began to change for the better and the marked thirst was noticed to decrease. By day 20, the new, much improved Lynn had finally evolved. Her grandparents couldn't believe the change in the child's personality. Her aunt made the familiar comment, 'It's like meeting the child for the first time!'

Lynn is still well and on her diet. In fact she is a proper little madam, politely refusing sweets and chocolate when they are offered at parties, and brings her own soft drinks and milk shakes for any special occasions. Interestingly, whenever small amounts of milk find their way into her diet she does not have any problems. However, when we elected on a two week trial of normal quantities of milk she was noticed to develop physical and behavourial symptoms by the third day. This is quite common. A high consumption of milk may bring on symptoms quite quickly whereas the occasional amount is tolerated. With one or two of the artificial colourings a reaction can occur much more rapidly, often within two hours of ingestion.

Claire and Roy

These children are sister and brother with very different but interesting allergy-related problems. Roy has asthma which has been shown to be due to a sensitivity to house dust mites and grass pollens. In addition he is extremely sensitive to tartrazine which is an artificial colouring added to orange drinks. Whenever he drinks (or even eats) anything containing tartrazine he develops a marked wheeze, sneeze and swelling eyelids. His parents were able to track down the problem additive themselves after careful investigation of his wheezing episodes. In fact it was only after they had positively identified the food additive connection to Roy's asthma episodes that they looked also at Claire's diet. Claire was not strictly hyperactive in that her features were only sporadic in nature. However when they occurred they were very dramatic. Her mother described the situation as follows; 'For some time I noticed that Claire could become unusually active and aggressive with a flushed face and glassy eyes. These episodes were not frequent, thank goodness, but sufficiently disturbing to make me wonder what was happening? Normally she is a very happy and easy going child but there seemed to be a real Jekyll and Hyde side to her character.' The true significance of these outbursts became obvious after Roy's tartrazine sensitivity had been established. Claire's parents began to record the foods and drink she consumed and scrutinized closely all food labels to identify which additives were part of her diet. Within a month they had identified five separate food additives as provoking the change in Claire's behaviour, one of which was actually in a bottle of medicine prescribed by their doctor for an ear infection! Now that these particular chemicals are kept out of her diet Claire has been trouble free for over eighteen months. Her parents really consulted me to confirm their own observations and deductions, which were very accurate. Apart from highlighting the sporadic nature of the problem in some children, this case history underlines how important are parents' own observations on their children's health.

Behavioural Problems confused with Hyperactivity – two case histories

Recent publicity involving diet and behavioural problems in children has created much confusion and suspicion among the public. Irresponsible and widely exaggerated claims by those who should know better serve only to reinforce these suspicions and create antagonism among doctors. For those of us labouring against the indifference of the profession towards hyperactivity these claims are positively unhelpful.

The media attention has also given some parents a totally false impression of hyperactivity. Two families who visited me reflect this confusion.

Barry was aged 16 years and did not get on well with his 18-year-old brother. In fact the two were quite often involved in heated arguments which occasionally led to an exchange of blows. Needless to say their parents were very concerned about the situation but really did not have much of a clue as how to deal with it. The father read in a magazine about diet-related anti-social behaviour and decided that Barry must have a similar problem. Armed with the article, father, mother and Barry trooped in to see me one rather wet wintry evening. Barry looked distinctly hostile and was obviously much aggrieved at being taken to a strange doctor. As the story unfolded it was quite obvious that the boy's behaviour had nothing whatsoever to do with diet. He got on well with his fellow students and teachers at school and was a great team game player. He had no past history of allergy, nor was there a family history of allergy. In fact the only time Barry let loose was when the older boy teased him. On the Symptom Score Card, he would barely have managed a score of two. As the consultation developed it turned out that the older boy was the 'bright light' of the family while Barry was more of a plodder and good with his hands. The boy's father delegated almost all responsibility to his wife, who had poor insight into the sibling rivalry. The older boy really did torment Barry and deserved any revenge that was exacted!

Despite having the situation thus assessed by an outsider (with no axe to grind) the parents were very upset at my interpretation. They took the comments as personal criticism and stormed out of the office. Barry stayed behind long enough to thank me for putting his side of the story forward for the first time! I have often wondered what became of this family — it wouldn't surprise me if they put both boys on special diets out of spite!

By contrast, the second problem was much more straight-forward. This family had lived in the United States for some years before moving to Ireland. The father worked in a multinational company and the transfer was one of the many moves up the corporate ladder. They had a seven-year-old daughter called Emma who began to go through a personality change — slowly but surely — after they had settled in their new home. Emma's mother described her as moody with tummy aches and limb pains. As so often is the case, the chance reading of an article on diet and children's behaviour prompted this visit.

Emma had lived in Florida before the move to Ireland which is a warm, sunny area of America. Unfortunately the weather in Ireland is nothing like that and so Emma was not in the outdoors as much as before. Within six months of arrival she had developed asthma, put down initially to the change of climate, from a warm and sunny summer to a cold and damp winter. The doctor treating her decided to try tablets designed to open the lungs and ease the asthma. They certainly worked very well and before long her chest was much better. However, in contrast to her asthma improvement, the child's moods became gloomy and she developed pains in the head, limbs and tummy.

At this stage Emma's mother took her off all milk to see if this would make any difference. The reasoning behind this was sound. The magazine article had listed the many symptoms of milk allergy in children, which included asthma, headaches, tummy and limb pains. Emma was drinking much more milk than she had been in Florida and the milk was richer. She had become very fond of the creamier Irish product! Consequently her mother wondered whether the child's ill-health was due to the increased consumption of a different, richer milk product. The results were disappointing and neither her mood nor her chest improved while off milk.

After this story was related to me I made enquiries about Emma's infant feeding pattern. I quickly concluded that milk had nothing to do with her symptoms at all. I was more interested in the tablets she was taking for her asthma. These were one of the theophylline preparations (theophylline is the name given to a group of drugs used in asthma management), and in susceptible children they can cause side-effects such as those experienced by Emma. As an experiment I took Emma off the tablets and put her on a spray inhaler for the asthma. Allergy testing revealed her to be very sensitive to house dust mites (these are tiny, microscopic insects which live off household dust particles and are quite often a cause of asthma when inhaled) and so special precautions were suggested to minimize the exposure to these insects.

Within a week the child was back to her usual self and free from most of her symptoms. The spray inhaler kept her asthma under control and allowed her to lead a normal life. As Emma was returning to Florida in six months from the time of our consultation there was little point in desensitizing her to house dust mites. She would be back to sunny, warm outdoor activities again by the time any desensitization schedule would be taking effect.

Emma's ill-health was a mixture of allergy and drug side-effects. Her sensitivity to house dust mites was probably something she had had for years but the move to Ireland precipitated the symptoms. This is because she spent more time indoors, in centrally-heated, wall-to-wall-carpeted rooms which are a haven for house dust-mites. The relatively sudden exposure to an increased amount of dust-mites was enough to bring on her chest symptoms. The subsequent drug treatment of the asthma unfortunately had side-effects and these made the child depressed, gloomy and full of aches and pains. There was no relationship to her diet and her behaviour at all.

As you can see from these two case histories, the diet and behaviour link has to be carefully assessed in each child. Many other conditions can produce behaviour/mood changes in children, none of them related to diet at all. Extravagant claims only create confusion and disappointment for some families.

In the next chapter, I shall discuss what other features doctors look for when assessing a possible diet-related medical problem in children.

3

Behavioural Problems in Children –
Other Causes

Hyperactivity is a special diagnosis or label for the unusual pattern of behaviour which we described in Chapter 2. As we have glimpsed already and will see in greater detail in later chapters, many of these children will respond to a special diet. There are, however, other behavioural problems often confused with hyperactivity, which cannot be treated in this way. These are caused by such conditions as asthma; eczema; hayfever; migraine; Allergic Irritability Syndrome; deafness or glue ear; lead toxicity; brain damage; and certain drug therapies.

When a child is suspected hyperactive and is brought to the doctor for assessment, a physical examination is carried out which proceeds towards a diagnosis by ruling out the conditions listed above. Certainly it is most unhelpful and very unwise to describe a child as hyperactive while he is suffering from one of these other problems, and any treatment routine is likely to be unsuccessful in these circumstances. The features doctors look for are as follows:

Skin: evidence of eczema (a red, scaly, itchy skin condition) either on the body or just in the skin creases at the elbows and backs of knees; red earlobes; high colouring on the cheeks; dark circles under or around the eyes; puffiness of the skin around the eyes; and frowning.

Eyes: 'glassy-eyed' appearance; red, watery, itchy eyes; and persistent blinking.

Ears: evidence of fluid in the inner ear.

Nose: crease on the bridge of the nose; repeatedly rubbing or 'twitching' of the nose to relieve itch; sneezing; repeatedly blowing the nose; and swollen, itchy inside lining of the nose.

Mouth: mouth ulcers; and repeatedly opening the mouth to maximum level and 'wiggling' the lower jaw to ease an itch at the back of the throat.

Chest: evidence of chest deformity due to asthma; wheezing or coughing.

Abdomen: abnominal bloating.

Miscellaneous: child constantly thirsty and usually has a drink close by; reversed letters when writing; clumsy behaviour; poor co-ordination; and poor reading and spelling.

This collection of features reflects many conditions ranging from hyperactivity, asthma and eczema to allergic rhinitis. Some of them overlap in certain problems, for example a child with flexual eczema may also have asthma and allergic rhinitis and the individual features reflect a generalized allergic nature.

These other causes of behaviour problems in children are very important as they are generally much easier to manage than hyperactivity itself. Occasionally a true hyperactive may have one of these conditions as well in which case attention to both problems makes for a better overall result.

Let us now look at these other possibilities in some detail and see how they affect children's behaviour.

Asthma

This a common problem and recent studies have shown that many children with asthma are not being identified when they present to their family doctors with symptoms such as coughing, wheezing, etc. Indeed they tend to be prescribed repeated courses of antibiotics and cough bottles which are of no use whatsoever. The most frequently mistaken diagnoses offered are bronchitis, wheezy bronchitis and whooping cough.

Children with undiagnosed asthma tend to be moody, cranky and irritable. They are quite often anti-social, refusing to join in games with their friends, preferring non-physical activities. If their asthma is sufficiently troublesome they are anxious, apprehensive and generally unhappy. If you could experience the same misery that they go through then I very much doubt you would feel any better! They are constantly short of breath; unable to run around without becoming distressed, have repeated coughing bouts which leave them tired and worn out. They just cannot understand why they feel this way while all their friends seem to be so full of energy. It is quite amazing to watch how their personalities change for the better when they are identified and correctly treated. Let me give you an example.

While I was working in England, a very successful building contractor brought his 11-year-old son to see me. The father was a keen rugby player and couldn't understand why his boy wasn't following in his footsteps. In fact he confided that he worried the boy was 'queer' (homosexual). Almost in passing he remarked that the child was very 'chesty' and prone to bronchitis. It transpired that the boy had asthma and had in fact had it since he was a child. This had been mistakenly diagnosed as bronchitis over the years leaving the child constantly unwell. He wanted desperately to play rugby as hard and fast as his father encouraged, but the physical effort was more than he could manage. The boy's mother had an instinctive feeling that the child's ill-health kept him back and perhaps over-compensated for this in a protective way. As you can imagine, this reinforced the father's suspicions that his son was a 'mother's boy'. Because he couldn't play any games that required much effort he confined his activities to stamp collecting, chess and nature study. His father watched this in not-so-silent dismay. You can well imagine the conflicts that arose because of this situation — overprotective mother versus aggressive, uncomprehending, physical father! Caught in the middle is the child with so-called bronchitis, desperately wanting to do more to ease the situation. Within one month of his chest condition being correctly diagnosed and treated the change in the boy was dramatic. He became less introverted and moody, more outgoing and active. He began to test his new found lung power. After three months' treatment the child was completely free from asthma and able to run as long as he wished. The years of inactivity meant he lacked the natural skills of sport but he made up for this with enthusiasm. Indeed he now became involved in scrapes as he started to settle a few old scores where previously other children had made unkind comments about his inactivity. His father was delighted and amazed at the change, his mother completely stunned. It was obvious that the boy's physical and emotional development was being shaped by his chest condition. His moodiness, irritability and general demeanour changed for the better with correct treatment.

The same problems apply to children correctly diagnosed as having asthma but who are not properly treated. The effect of this condition is much greater than is generally accepted.

Drug therapy in asthma

As we saw in Chapter 2, the use of theophylline preparations in the treatment of asthma can cause mood changes, and if your child is on one of these and has some form of mood or behaviour problem it is well worth having this checked before looking at diet.

Eczema

Eczema is an allergic skin condition. The skin is dry, scaly, red and itchy. The most distressing part is the intense itch and subsequent scratching. Children who, for whatever reason, have poor control of their skin are also prone to frequent changes of mood. They are very irritable, easily upset and short-tempered. However, these unpleasant characteristics fade with proper skin control. If you or I had a constant itch, I doubt very much if we would be the most placid people to live with either!

Hay fever

Hay fever is the label used to describe a group of symptoms consisting of red, itchy watery eyes; blocked, itchy runny nose; coughing or wheezing. These features occur in the summer months when the pollen count is high and is due to an allergy to pollen. These features are commonly mistaken for 'summer colds'. Children with unrecognized or inadequately treated hay fever are irritable, cranky, short-tempered and often quite drowsy. In some cases the latter may be due to the drug therapy used in treatment.

Symptoms such as these, occurring on a seasonal basis and lasting the summer, reflect a behavioural pattern different to hyperactivity and due only to a pollen allergy. Proper management soon corrects all the features, including those of behaviour.

Helen suffered from asthma and hay fever for many years before her symptoms were correctly identified. Every June from the age of four she became irritable, grouchy, short-tempered and generally badly behaved. During the warm, sunny weeks of summer she avoided out-door activities, had streaming nose and eyes and sneezed a lot. In addition she coughed and wheezed all day long. Until Helen was nine years old these symptoms were incorrectly diagnosed as due to bronchitis or summer colds. Her behaviour pattern during the summer was so erratic and bizarre that her parents wondered if she had some psychological problem and even went so far as to seek help privately from a psychologist. Fortunately he referred her back to the family doctor for reassessment. After a long discussion it was decided that Helen should be seen by a paediatrician who cleared up the confusion very quickly. He correctly diagnosed Helen's symptoms as asthma and hay fever, and confirmed the diagnosis by allergy testing. With appropriate treatment Helen settled quickly and, in particular, had trouble-free summers from then on.

Migraine

Some children have constant headaches, quite often caused by foods such as milk or chocolate. They resent interference, noise or physical activity and withdraw into themselves. Problems arise when no obvious cause can be found for these symptoms and psychological causes are attributed. Children are often completely dependent on their parents to interpret their feelings. If they can convey the message that they have headaches all the time then they should be half-way towards a solution. However, if the parents take the child to their doctor and he can find nothing to explain away the symptoms the chances are they will be labelled tension or stress headaches. The parents are then left with two problems: headaches which they don't know how to deal with, and stress or tension in their child which is beyond their comprehension. As with un-diagnosed asthma, the sequence can become a spiral of misinformation, poor advice and inadequate treatment. Small wonder that the child has mood and behaviour problems!

Allergic Irritability Syndrome

This a new name for an old condition! However, it describes the situation perfectly. Children with this problem seem to get 'one cold after another', show marked moodswings, irritability and aggressive behaviour. Physical examination often reveals facial features such as swollen darkened circles around the eyes, an upward rubbing of the nose to relieve the itch, blocked nose and sneezing. Severely affected children are mistakenly labelled hyperactive or emotionally disturbed while in fact their problems are due to sensitivity to allergens such as moulds, pollens, dusts, etc. The predominant area of trouble is the nose, producing allergic rhinitis, but the eyes are often also affected with redness, itch and tearing. When these children are correctly diagnosed and skin-tested to identify the substances to which they are allergic, appropriate therapy can commence. When the child's physical problems are reversed the true, normal personality shows through.

Recently a classic example of this condition was described at an allergy conference in North America. A six year old blond haired, blue-eyed boy had a history of mood swings, irritability and aggressive behaviour. He also suffered from recurring 'colds' and was constantly grouchy. Examination revealed features characteristic of long standing allergic rhinitis (allergy of the lining of the nose). He had dark rings around his eyes, a crease on the bridge of the nose from repeated rubbing, blocked nose and general puffiness of the eyes. Allergy tests showed that the boy was allergic to grasses, weeds, trees, dust and moulds. After a period of treatment the child's physical symptoms improved dramatically with the mood swings and temper tantrums no longer a problem. When he was briefly taken off medication by his parents, all of the above symptoms returned. He was successfully managed over a three year period and no longer required treatment. He is also still free from the behaviour problems. The specialist who presented this case history commented that untreated allergy leads to irritability and grouchiness in adults but, as children are less able to deal with the discomfort, they show a disruptive pattern of behaviour.

Deafness

Children — especially very allergic children — may develop fluid in the inner ear which acts as a barrier to sound. There are many causes of this condition (referred to as 'glue ear') but the end result is always the same — partial or total loss of hearing. It is the partial deafness that creates most problems as parents and teachers mistake the child's lack of response as disobedience. A simple example will illustrate this point. The child is sitting in front of the TV, hard of hearing, perhaps following a bad head cold. He turns the volume up and his mother screams at him to turn it down. He doesn't hear her and she clips him round the ear for ignoring her! He is stunned. All he can understand is that his mother hit him for ignoring her when he was quite certain she never said a word! Multiply this grievance by the number of times it happens on a daily basis and you will have some idea of how personalities change. Throw in a comment of 'stupid' at school when he cannot answer the question he cannot hear properly and the stage is set for a major emotional problem. These children become angry, sensitive and aggressive. Changing the diet makes no difference — their hearing deficit must be identified and corrected immediately. Suspect this in your child if he appears to ignore requests or commands out of his range of vision; or if he regularly turns the volume up when watching TV or seems to be watching your mouth and not your eyes when you talk to him.

Lead Toxicity

This a favourite suggestion of some advisers in the Hyperactive Children Support Groups. I have never been convinced of its significance in the behavioural problems of children but include it as a possible *rare* cause in case it may be important in any one child. Seriously high levels of lead in the body can lead to very distressing features such as epileptic fits and unconsciousness. Even after recovery there may be evidence of permanent brain damage.

Subtle forms of lead toxicity (i.e. levels of lead in the body higher than are safe for good health) may lead to behaviour problems similar to hyperactivity. Children at risk from this problem are those who might be exposed to high levels of lead in their environment. This might occur in homes built before the 1950s as most house paints contained lead then. In addition, children living in areas with soft water are potentially at risk as lead pipes may leak some of the lead into the water more easily in these conditions. Lead compounds may be released into the air during some industrial process and of course lead is discharged in car exhaust fumes.

If you are concerned about the potential hazards of lead pollution in your area, have your child assessed by the family doctor with a blood test. *Do not waste your time and money on hair analysis — this procedure is positively useless.*

Brain Damage

The brain is the nerve centre of the body. It controls and co-ordinates physical movements, and our thoughts and emotions originate here. Different areas of the brain have different functions and consequently any permanent damage to these areas might cause bizarre mental or physical activity. For example, scarring of the brain tissue at the centre where physical movements originate can often cause epileptic fits. Consequently brain damage at different areas might produce a variety of symptoms such as overactivity, poor co-ordination and impaired psychological development. This theory is not always easy to prove and more often than not is assumed to be the cause of hyperactivity. Where brain damage can be definitely shown in a child any behaviour problems may well be related to the injury. However, a brain damaged child is just as likely to have problems with diet as a normal child and often this link is ignored.

In addition, certain children with inherited brain disorders (e.g. Down's Syndrome) may have their behaviour problems overlooked when, again, these too are likely to have a dietary cause.

Drug Treatments

Children on long term treatments for conditions such as

epilepsy and asthma may have behaviour problems due to medication. As we saw with Emma in Chapter 2, mood changes in asthmatics may be caused by the drugs used in treating their chest condition. The same problem may arise in the management of other long term illnesses, for example epilepsy or arthritis. The drugs used in epilepsy can occasionally interfere with normal brain activity, producing symptoms of agitation, confusion and poor co-ordination. In addition some children become withdrawn and moody. Anti-arthritis drugs can also alter mood, although usually this is described as 'being below par'. For some children the arthritis drugs produce physical discomfort such as nausea and abdominal pains which add to the general feeling of being unwell. Needless to say the child's behaviour in such circumstances is often less than angelic.

As you can see there are quite a few important causes of aberrant behaviour problems in children and each child should be fully assessed before a firm diagnosis is made. In the Appendices of this book I have set out Symptom Score Cards for the most important of these conditions. This will enable you to assess your child's symptoms yourself and decide if he or she fits one of these categories.

4

The Importance of Diet in Hyperactivity

The hyperactive child is now at the crossroads of management. He has been correctly identified using the symptom score card and any other concurrent medical conditions diagnosed as well. At this point he is likely to be referred for assessment and treatment. The treatment might take the form of psychotherapy, behaviour modification or drug therapy. This is the crucial point at which to give the child a trial of a special diet for a minimum period of three months. The other treatment regimes can be started if the dietary trial is unsuccessful but three months is not too long to defer them in the child's interest. Indeed the other routines will be continued for a good deal longer than three months without any dramatic improvement being obvious. With a special diet the results, if any, should be obvious at the end of the time allowed.

As I have mentioned earlier in this book, the role of diet in the management of hyperactivity is a hotly disputed subject. The dispute is mainly between parents and health professionals. The latter group are still very suspicious of diets and believe the enthusiasts of this routine only cloud the issue and interfere with the correct approach.

Recent research in England and Australia has shown a definite link between overactive behaviour patterns in children and their diet. The English study was a spin-off from an investigation where researchers examined the link between migraine and diet in children. Investigators found that 93 per cent of the 88 children in their study became headache-free on a special, very restricted diet. As other foods were added, the headaches returned and by careful painstaking observation the problem foods were finally identified. The study concluded that most children with severe, frequent migraine recover on an appropriate diet.

As this study reached conclusion a number of interesting 'side-effects' were discovered. For example, the parents of seven children taking part in the trial were so impressed with the results that they were also successfully treated for headaches by diet! However a most interesting result was the number of associated symptoms which also cleared. These included tummy pains, behaviour disorders, epileptic fits, asthma, eczema and limb pains.

I spoke with one of the dietitians involved in this study who told me that many of the researchers had reluctantly agreed to take part in the study. They were sceptical of the diet–ill-health link and felt that the trial was a waste of time and money. All of the doubters were astonished with the final results and sufficiently impressed to try a dietary approach to other, long-term problems in children. One of these new studies involved testing the theory that certain foods may be responsible for epileptic fits in children. Here, too, the results were impressive. On the very restricted diet, 53 per cent of the 53 children with epilepsy in the study stopped having fits, 13 per cent had fewer fits, and 79 per cent reported an overall improvement in associated symptoms, such as headaches, and tummy pains. The foods found to trigger convulsions included milk, cheese, citrus fruits, and chocolate. These results are not very dissimilar to the trial involving migraine sufferers where the most troublesome foods were milk, eggs, chocolate, oranges, wheat and benzoic acid (a food additive).

Finally the same researchers investigated the role of diet in hyperactive children. A total of 76 children were selected for an in-depth study and put on a very restricted diet (called an oligo-antigenic diet — this is explained below). Of these, 62 improved, and a normal range of behaviour was achieved in 21. Other symptoms, such as headaches, tummy pains and fits also improved. Of the 62 children who improved on the restricted diet, 28 were selected for tests to identify the foods actually responsible for their behaviour problems. At the end of the study a total of 48 foods were incriminated, artificial colourants and preservatives being the most frequent offenders. However, no child was sensitive to these alone.

The method of testing foods in this way is briefly as follows: The children are first put on an oligo-antigenic diet. This is a very, very restricted diet containing only those foods considered to be 'safe', that is, not involved in causing hyperactivity. The safe foods used in the study were lamb, chicken, potatoes, rice, bananas, apples, brassica vegetables, water, calcium and vitamin supplements. The children were kept on this diet for four weeks during which time most improved considerably. After that other foods were reintroduced weekly, one at a time, and the responses noted. At the end of this stage the troublesome foods were identified and listed. A further, more detailed and rather technical study was then performed to prove conclusively that these foods were indeed producing behaviour problems. This confirmed the earlier results.

The foods which produced symptoms were (in descending order of frequency of involvement): artificial colours and preservatives, cow's milk, chocolate, grapes, wheat, oranges, cheese, eggs, peanuts, maize, fish, oats, melons, tomatoes, ham/bacon, pineapple, sugar, beef, beans, peas, malt, apples, pork, chicken, potatoes, tea, coffee, cucumbers, bananas, carrots, peaches, lamb, turkey, rice, yeast, apricots and onions. Some of the children who reacted to cow's milk also reacted to one of the milk substitutes. The foods to which there was no reaction were cabbage, lettuce, cauliflower, celery, goat's cheese, duck eggs. Five of the children were noticed to have symptoms with certain inhaled substances – pollen, perfume and house dust.

There are two immediate observations on this trial: first, the astonishing number of foods involved, and second it becomes clearer why the Feingold diet alone was not completely effective. Ben Feingold placed much emphasis on the role of salicylate containing foods and artificial food additives as provocatives to overactivity in children. Important as these are there are many other foods involved in the condition which the Feingold diet did not exclude. In addition he actually encouraged a higher intake of some of these products to make up for the restrictions already imposed by his diet.

Consequently many children were only partially 'treated' by the Feingold diet and did not improve significantly enough for further dietary measures to be considered. Identifying the problem foods in food intolerance is a bit like opening a combination lock. Unless all the numbers are correct and together then the lock stays closed. So too with hyperactivity and diets – for most children all the troublesome foods need to be removed and all at the one time for the complete restoration of normal behaviour and activity.

Another interesting feature of this study was that the number of definitely allergic children and non-allergic was the same in both response and non-response to diet. This is very important as too much emphasis may be laid on the allergic nature of children who are hyperactive. The diet–behaviour link seems to apply equally to those showing and not showing an allergic tendency.

In Australia, at Sydney University, a similar study was performed which again confirmed a link between certain foodstuffs and overactive behaviour. While the Australian doctors came to different conclusions as to how this actually happens, the net result is still a positive diet–behaviour relationship. These researchers believe that salicylate-containing foods are the main culprits and that the behavioural responses depend on the quantity and frequency of their consumption.

While the experts may argue as to the exact mechanisms of action in the diet–hyperactivity link, there is sufficient information now available to devise a treatment programme for affected children.

The Hyperactive Child Treatment Programme

Once you have completed the symptom score card on page 12 and confirmed the strong possibility of hyperactivity in your child then a management scheme should be decided on. The approach presented below is logical, sensible, thorough and should be followed carefully. Give the programme a trial of at least three months to take effect. Within this time–scale most hyperactive children can be successfully managed and their behaviour–activity problems eased.

The rationale behind the approach is simple: it aims to eliminate those foods and drinks containing artificial additives known to be responsible for hyperactivity in children, it aims to cut back or remove other foodstuffs also likely to be involved in hyperactivity, it aims to identify and treat any medical conditions that could contribute to behaviour problems and finally it aims to identify and manage any other allergens involved in the child's overall medical condition.

The first step is to eliminate all processed foods where practical and, in particular, to avoid all foods and drinks which contain the following additives:

E102 Tartrazine
E104 Quinoline Yellow
E107 Yellow 2G
E110 Sunset Yellow
E123 Amaranth
E124 Ponceau 4R
E127 Erythrosine
E150 Caramel
E210–219 Benzoates and Benzoic Acid
E249 Potassium nitrite
E250 Sodium nitrite
E251 Sodium nitrate
E320 Butylated hydroxyanisole (BHA)
E321 Butylated hydroxytoluene (BHT)
E621 Monosodium glutamate (MSG)

E622 Monopotassium glutamate
E623 Calcium glutamate

The E numbers represent the chemicals added in foodstuffs and should be on the labels of whatever packaging or bottling the food is contained in. Additives which are mentioned on labels are usually listed according to their function in the food e.g. preservative, emulsifier. Quite often the exact name of the chemical in question will be replaced by the serial number (or E number), as in preservative E200.

Eliminate or cut down considerably on foods which contain natural amounts of salicylates. These include the following:

Dried fruits	Endives
Berry fruits	Olives
Oranges	Grapes
Apricots	Almonds
Pineapples	Liquorice
Cucumbers	Peppermints
Gherkins	Honey
Tomato sauce	Worcester sauce
Tea	

Salicylates are also found in aspirin and aspirin-containing medicine (may be labelled as sodium salicylate). Many over-the-counter cough bottles have aspirin in them and should be avoided; if an analgesic is required use only paracetamol (Panadol).

In addition to foods and drinks containing these substances all medicinal syrups or tablets coloured orange, red, green and yellow should be avoided. Any other medicines, toothpastes, vitamin preparations, pastilles and lozenges containing synthetic flavouring and colourings are out as well.

As part of an overall review of the child's diet and encouragement towards healthier foods all unnecessary sweets, cakes, fizzy drinks etc., should be avoided. This will include ice cream, ice lollies, sweets, chocolates, soft drinks, drink mixes, flavoured drinks, jellies, cakes, dessert mixes, biscuits, jams, pastries, potato crisps, prepared chips, etc. While this may seem an unnecessarily harsh requirement the end results justify the effort. In particular it reinforces the message to child and parents that junk foods are out and wholesome foods are in. Even if it never worked in hyperactivity (and it does) the routine is much healthier all round.

It is a good idea at this initial stage to record the total score your child reached on the symptom score card. When you review this total at the end of the treatment programme you should be pleasantly surprised at the dramatic drop in the score.

The second stage is to eliminate suspect foods over and above those already mentioned. If your child has other symptoms such as headaches, tummy pains, limb pains, asthma or eczema there is a good chance these are due to other foods. Top of the list of culprits is cow's milk and associated milk products. Suspect a milk intolerance if your child suffered in infancy or still suffers from three or more of the following complaints:

Colic
Irritability
Repeated Vomiting
Diarrhoea/constipation
Snuffly nose
Chestiness or asthma
Eczema
Poor sleep pattern
Hives
Persisting bad nappy rashes.

If a milk intolerance is suspected then milk and all milk products should be eliminated from the diet. This really applies to milk in its pure form such as milk for drinking, cream, cheese, yoghourt, butter, etc. Even if your child does not show three or more of the above features of milk intolerance but still consumes a lot of milk or milk products then cut back on these to the equivalent of a half glass daily. If your child has atopic eczema in addition to hyperactivity you should also eliminate eggs, fish and peanuts and cut down on or avoid beef products.

Next you need to have the child assessed for co-existing medical conditions which are not being adequately treated (such as partial deafness or asthma) and ensure that these are corrected. Again check that any drugs prescribed will not add to or aggravate the hyperactivity. In particular check that syrups and tablets etc. are additive free.

Finally check that your child is assessed by allergy testing for any other significant allergens and managed accordingly. The easiest and safest allergy routine involves a technique known as skin prick testing. This procedure will identify important inhalant allergens such as dust, moulds, pollens, danders and foods. The tests for foods are unfortunately not very reliable and usually require further checking. Your doctor will advise you on this but full details are available in my book *How to Cope with Your Child's Allergies,* published also by Sheldon Press.

Having got this far, most children show a significant improvement. Some may still have occasional outbursts and if they also have had no clearance of their marked thirst then Evening Primrose Oil should be given. Evening Primrose Oil is an essential fatty acid rich in linoleic acid and gamma linoleic acid. For reasons still unknown the addition of this product into the diet of some hyperactive children, particularly those with thirst as a symptom, is an extra help in management.

There are a few important points to be aware of regarding this routine:

1. There may be an initial deterioration in symptoms – bear with this, the child should improve after five to seven days.
2. Some children are able to tolerate the offending foods in reduced quantities after a few months.
3. Response to diet is poor in families where adverse psychological or social problems exist.
4. The diet is not a punishment routine.

5. Other members of the family may benefit from a similar approach, as food allergy often runs in families.
6. The greatest cheating is usually not by the child but is initiated by relatives, grandparents, neighbours who think the approach ridiculous and actively encourage the use of forbidden foods.

The diet is restrictive in some senses but worth the effort. Because each child is an individual and with unique features, I can give no hard and fast rules as to how long the routine should be maintained. As a general rule, the problem foods should be eliminated for at least twelve months.

An alternative to the above approach is the oligo-antigenic diet. This means using a very, very restricted list of foods for about ten days and then re-introducing other foods, one at a time, on a weekly basis and observing any reactions. This routine is not without hazards and should only be contemplated if a trained dietitian is involved and willing to help all the way. I rarely use this approach.

Conclusion

A three month dietary trial for management of hyperactivity in children is worth considering before embarking upon other therapies. The diet involves a return to more wholesome foods and the avoidance of specific, troublesome foods. In addition, existing medical problems are identified and corrected. Using this approach a considerable proportion, if not the majority, of hyperactive children improve at least to the point where they are manageable. Those children who do not respond may well benefit from the other therapies currently in use (see Chapter 5).

Food Sensitivities

Most people find it hard to accept that foodstuffs can affect a child's behaviour. Because of the widespread recent publicity about the problem there is an understandable suspicion that the whole idea is nonsense. Certainly some of the more extravagant claims have served only to reinforce these doubts and belittle the credibility of those working to make sense of the situation. Doctors, too, are having difficulty coming to terms with the diet–hyperactivity concept.

It is important to recognize that the problem is not widespread. While there are no statistics available on the prevalence of the condition it would appear to be in the 1–2 per cent range. These children appear to be either very sensitive to the foods concerned or to a build-up of their breakdown constituents. This sensitivity is often very difficult to pinpoint accurately, but the exact mechanisms of effect are now becoming clear. The following are the most likely causes of food sensitivities in children and adults.

Allergic effect: This means that a consitituent of the food involved provokes an allergic response in the body. For example one of the proteins found in milk, called casein, is often involved in the allergic response to milk.

Pharmacologic effect: This means that the food or a constituent of the food acts like a drug. We recognize that certain drugs stimulate and others sedate. It is possible that some food additives have a drug-like activity causing overstimulation.

Toxic effect: This means that a build-up occurs in the body of the food or one of its breakdown products. It is possible that some salicylate-containing foods only cause problems if consumed frequently and in high amounts, producing toxic levels in the body.

Idiosyncratic effect: This means that there is a peculiarly individual response to the foodstuff that is unlikely to happen to other people.

Psychological effect: Some people are so convinced that certain foods are bad for them that they can provoke symptoms whenever such foods are consumed. They very often tolerate the food completely if it is disguised in some form and consumed.

Enzyme deficiency: Enzymes are chemicals which the body produces to help us break down certain foods into a more absorbable form. Occasionally these chemicals are absent and the foods reach areas of the intestine in a form which is not usually found. This can trigger a wide range of symptoms.

In hyperactivity the most likely explanations involve allergic, pharmacologic, toxic and idiosyncratic effects. It is equally possible that some children have all four mechanisms while others may be over stimulated by one only. In the study performed at the Hospital for Sick Children in London, a wide variety of foods was found to trigger behavioural abnormalities in hyperactive children. It was postulated that these reactions had an allergic basis although the researchers kept an open mind about other possible mechanisms of action. Almost half of the children who took part in this study had a definitely proven allergic nature. However, the number who responded to a special diet with a reduction in activity was no greater among the allergic children than the non-allergic. This immediately suggests we should not rely too heavily on an allergic nature as being the most important feature of the condition.

In Australia, at the Department of Human Nutrition at Sydney University, researchers also studied the diet and hyperactivity link. They came to similar conclusions but suggested different reasons for their results. The Australian team point out that certain foods contain naturally occurring amounts of chemicals such as salicylates and monosodium glutamate. If these foods (and others containing artificial additives) are eaten in combination or on several successive days the chemicals involved accumulate. If they pass a certain threshold, symptoms occur in those children who are extremely sensitive. The doctors believe that the reaction is pharmacological, i.e. the chemicals act like a drug and have a stimulating effect.

At a different centre in Australia (the CSIRO Division of Food Research in New South Wales), researchers investigating the hyperactivity–diet link came up with another and different explanation for the condition. They feel that there may be an accumulation of a substance called P-cresol which may be toxic to the nervous system. (Certainly P-cresol has been conclusively shown to be toxic to the nervous system of rodents in experimental studies.) P-cresol is an end-product of tyrosine metabolism and tyrosine is an important compound which is present in many protein foods. The theory is that children consuming large quantities of tyrosine may build up excessive levels of its breakdown product, P-cresol. Milk is the source of dietary tyrosine most readily accessible to children and is also present in a variety of food products. The build-up of P-cresol may cause an overstimulation of the brain leading to hyperactivity. This fits in with the observation of parents that removing or cutting back on milk helps their overactive children.

This particular theory has gained support from researchers at Queen Charlotte's Hospital in London who discovered that certain food constituents (especially food additives) impair the usual (natural) methods which the body has for getting rid of P-cresol. Consequently the food additives are important suspects in this piece of detective work.

As you can see, the theories can become very technical and complicated and perhaps difficult to understand. What is important, though, is that the evidence is at last accumulating to back up the claims of the Hyperactive Child Support Group (and others) of the diet–hyperactivity link. While we may have to wait a bit longer for the researchers to reach definite conclusions, their interim results give great heart to those of us pursuing a cure through diet.

5

Other Therapies in Hyperactivity

If every hyperactive child achieved a normal behaviour pattern on a special diet the problem would be solved completely. However many do not or they reach a certain level beyond which no dietary manipulation can improve. What is important at this point is to accept this fact and not go chasing other cult diets or therapies in some vain search for an easy answer. Better instead to concentrate on a structured approach to the child's behaviour and be guided by the health professionals trained in this task. Some of these people are quite happy to go along with the three-month dietary trial and accept whatever results (good or bad) that might be achieved. If the child reaches an acceptable level of behaviour then he is one less to deal with and one for whom other therapies are unnecessary. If he reaches a better level but is still not manageable then the dietary approach can be combined with one of the other routines. This seems to me to be only common sense and unlikely to offend anyone's beliefs on the subject. I can see no value in breaking the diet if some gains have been achieved just to concentrate on a different approach.

The following are the choices of health professionals likely to deal with hyperactive children. Which one will be suitable for your child is an individual decision and you should be guided by your family doctor in this regard.

Child psychiatrist: A doctor specializing in the psychological disorders of children. He can prescribe drugs but may prefer to use psychotherapy (see below). In general, these doctors deal with children with a specific, identifiable psychological disorder.

Paediatrician: A doctor specializing in the health care of children. Most paediatricians prefer to deal only with physical illness but some specialize in disorders of learning and behaviour as well.

Clinical psychologist: Not usually a medical doctor although sometimes actually called 'doctor'. He will have studied psychology and tend to use psychotherapy or behaviour-therapy treatment routines.

Educational psychologist: Interested in the way children cope with school, and very helpful in dealing with the special educational needs of hyperactive children.

Treatment Routines

Each hyperactive child is an individual with special problems, unique features and individual requirements. The type of therapy that any one child might require will depend on such a range of factors that it is impossible to describe anything other than general guidelines on the therapies available.

Psychotherapy: A method of psychological treatment where children are helped to understand their own difficulties. This may involve the whole family, especially if it is felt that tensions in the family unit are creating problems. This routine would obviously not be of great use in small children unless their parents and older brothers or sisters were involved.

Behaviour modification: This is not easy to describe because of the complex nature of the therapy and the variation in technique of its practitioners. One format is known as 'goal and reward' — implying that certain attainable goals are set for the child to achieve and a suitable reward offered if he succeeds.

Drug therapy: This form of treatment is more common in North America than in Britain or Ireland. The medications used are of the stimulant variety (called amphetamines) and can help hyperactive children concentrate for longer periods and reduce their impulsive nature. When on this therapy most hyperactive children are quieter and more in control of themselves. It may seem illogical that stimulant drugs will help hyperactivity but, for whatever reason, they do. The exact mechanism of effect is unknown. These medications are not habit-forming in children but are associated with occasional side-effects which include: depression/'tearfulness', headaches; sleeplessness; and lack of appetite. Only the specialists dealing with the child can decide when to try this routine and how long it should last. With careful selection the results in hyperactivity are good.

6

Coping with a
Hyperactive Child
by *Sarah Nichols*

Sarah Nichols is the founder member and secretary of the Hyperactive Child Support Group in Ireland. She has a child with hyperactivity and it was through her search for help for him that she became aware of the Feingold diet and theory. She founded the Hyperactive Child Support Group in 1980 and it has since become a registered charity.

Bringing up children is a full-time job and never completely easy. As a mother, you will use your natural instincts and sense but may draw on your own upbringing and the standards of your parents. However, your own personal touches and preferences will shine through and the net result is a fusion of old and new ideas, hopefully producing a happy family unit.

Then something goes horribly wrong. One of your children becomes terribly disruptive and repeatedly upsets the family life. He is unashamedly disobedient, seems always to have the upper hand, refuses to comply with any suggestion and breaks every rule and routine. His behaviour is so bad that friends stop calling round and even avoid mentioning him in conversation. You feel isolated.

At first it is hard to accept that there really is a problem but as the situation persists and begins to cause physical and mental exhaustion the implications of the behaviour pattern can no longer be avoided. The strain on your marriage and the other children mean that something must be done. As parents you have no alternative but to look after the child so you get on with adjusting to the extra labour and vigilance necessary until this becomes the norm. But the most difficult hurdle of all to overcome is to accept that there is a problem and that it will not go away. It really is a heartbreak to admit that your otherwise apparently healthy child is almost a monster made flesh. However, the sooner the situation is accepted, assessed and tackled the better for all concerned.

My own feelings towards my own hyperactive son have been very mixed. He is my third child. I looked forward to his arrival, thinking his babyhood would be very easy, having been through it all on two previous occasions. I was going to relax and enjoy him totally. But the reality turned out rather different. I struggled from the start, loving and hating the boy, trying to keep one step ahead of him, until by the age of three his behaviour was too much for me and I was advised by my GP to seek help.

It was hard to face up to the situation but I was reassured by some that he would grow out of it. The immediate reaction of family and friends was that I was becoming obsessed, neurotic and overprotective, and that I should relax a bit more. He became more and more impossible and as the years slipped by he showed no signs of growing out of it.

By the time I started to accept the situation I was very debilitated and low. It was a sad time and I was depressed. The discovery that I might be able to help my child by putting him on a special diet came as a breath of fresh air, lifting me and spurring me on with a new enthusiasm. I felt I was doing something positive, which eased my lingering guilt feelings. The fact that it worked was a bonus. There are inevitable infringements of the diet which we can cope with but the bad moments soon pass and are forgotten.

There have been occasions when I have been close to battering the boy. Fortunately I am still stronger than he is, but he does from time to time show bruises. These occasions and feelings absolutely shatter me, though they are, I am assured, normal in the circumstances.

Undoubtedly my older children resent the disturbed family

life but in spite of the ups and downs, they are caring and supportive.

What to do

Handling the hyperactive child requires attention both to diet and to discipline. A child learns by copying and follows the good or bad examples set by his parents. Children are resilient and alert, rarely missing anything and they are quick to turn things to their own advantage. It is important to maintain a feeling of calm control even though you may not feel it; and it is better to live for the moment, minute by minute. Try not to plan ahead, since an event you are looking forward to often falls flat, leading to bitter disappointment.

At the beginning trust your natural instincts and do not be put down or brushed off by unsympathetic health professionals. If your baby is not feeding well, or has constant colic and cannot be comforted — have this investigated. If the baby is in pain, the only way he can ask for help is by crying. If the pain persists then the crying may become more intense and prolonged. As the months go by this may lead on to moaning, rocking to and fro and even head-banging. The longer this is ignored (or put up with) the greater the chances of prolonged problems.

If your child is older and more adventurous in his eating habits then follow these personally tried guidelines.

1. Give the diet a chance — but try and find a sympathetic doctor who will give you help in this regard.
2. Get back to home-made, wholesome meals and encourage regular eating habits. Ensure the child is hungry for meals — so no in-between snacks.
3. Try and ensure adequate rest, fresh air and exercise.
4. Make sure the house is safe; if necessary put perspex on vulnerable windows, and do not leave valuable objects and dangerous tools lying around. Put high locks on doors.

5. When you say 'no' you must mean it. Be consistent if possible and try and ensure total co-operation on this with all the family members (including uncles, aunts, etc.). Try at all costs to remain calm, speaking in a soft controlled voice. Discourage excessive noise and too much talking all at once. Hyperactive children may have a learning disability and too much noise and chatter is threatening, especially if they cannot keep pace with the activities or comprehend the conversation.

6. If possible ignore bad behaviour — or at least do not lose your temper. On the other hand reward good behaviour — more often than not the hyperactive child is ignored or pushed aside, leading to poor self-esteem. It is important to give praise when it is deserved.

7. Try to arrange some help. This means having someone who will respect the dietary changes. It is essential to have some time for yourself, even if it is only to do the weekly shopping in comfort. In the evening resume a hobby or embark on an evening class or take up a musical instrument. Have a couple of friends in for a meal and/or game of cards. Make an effort to resume your own life. The effect of the improved diet will make the child easier to deal with and will help the child sleep better, thus allowing you to devote some time to yourself in the evening.

8. When selecting schools, make sure the classes are not too large. This may mean going to a private school.

9. Encourage quiet moments. Put the child into a fully supported position in sitting or lying, and encourage deep breathing. Breathe in through the nose allowing the abdomen to rise, breathe out through the mouth letting the abdomen relax and pull in. This is particularly helpful after a tantrum to restore equilibrium.

10 Do try the diet for three months at least. It is healthy and safe — you have nothing to lose. In fact it is a positive contribution to the health of your family, but more importantly it will also help if you remember one basic

thing — your child's hyperactivity is something you have to cope with, it is not something for which you have to blame yourself.

7

The Hyperactive Child
Support Group

Self-help groups are usually formed to give support to victims
(and their families) of one of the many long term illnesses.
There are self-help societies dealing with asthma, eczema,
psoriasis, schizophrenia, multiple sclerosis, arthritis, etc. Each
of the conditions that these societies represent are those for
which conventional medicine does not have a cure. The victims
often feel, rightly or wrongly, that doctors have given up on
their problem or are unlikely to help them beyond a certain
point.

Whatever the reasons for coming together, self-help groups
are a source of great comfort and advice for fellow sufferers.
Tips on management are exchanged, ideas on treatment
discussed and guest speakers often invited to lecture on the
relevant condition. Perhaps the greatest benefit comes from the
ability to share fears, worries and difficulties with others who
may have gone through it all before.

The Hyperactive Child Support Group was founded out of
frustration at the indifference of the medical profession towards
the condition. I would imagine that few societies have had to
put up with the ridicule and hostility from health professionals
that this group did. Despite (or even because of) this
antagonism the group quickly grew. With each snippet of
publicity, more families came 'out of the woodwork' and it soon
became obvious that hyperactivity in children was not as rare as
had been previously claimed.

Branches of the Hyperactive Child Support Group now exist
in many countries throughout the world — reflecting the
widespread prevalence of the condition — and the amount of
good work they do is considerable. They have been the last
resort of many distraught parents and often the best source of

advice. The aims of the Hyperactive Child Support Group are to help and support hyperactive children and their parents (although not financially); encourage the formation of local groups or contacts where parents may get together for mutual support and understanding; urge the medical profession, health and education authorities to take more interest in the day-to-day problems of hyperactive children and adolescents; promote urgent research into causes of hyperactivity whether it be linked to chemical food additives, nutritional deficiencies, food allergies and/or environmental pollution; and press for early and proper diagnosis of hyperactivity, possible treatments and management and to disseminate information to all interested parties.

In addition to these commendable aims the Hyperactive Support Group has been vocal in drawing attention to the poor dietary habits of children in westernized countries. In my opinion they have led the way in this regard. Doctors, nutritionists, and the media have not been slow to follow, with newspapers, radio and television nowadays running regular features on diet. In Britain, *The Times* (4 April 1986) reported on a survey of 3,000 children aged 10–15 years which reflected how poor dietary habits are. The findings of the survey showed that children eat more chips, crisps and snacks than any other single food such as meat or fish. They eat ten times more white bread than wholemeal bread, consume too many sugary drinks and take too little fruit and fresh vegetables. Children thus risk serious illness later in life through the consumption of such fatty and sugary foods. More to the point, their diet may already be contributing to ill-health in the form of overactive behaviour in those susceptible to the problem.

The Hyperactive Child Support Group has also lobbied consistently for the removal of unnecessary additives in food manufacturing. Despite repeated reassurances on the safety of these chemicals from experts, general unease has developed in most people's minds as to the need for them and their possible effect on health. (We will go into greater detail on this subject in the next chapter.) In response to increased consumer demands for additive-free foods the food industry is now producing more chemical-free products and advertising this fact regularly. Packaged foods now claim in bold letters to be 'free from artificial colourings and preservatives', where years ago such information was considered unnecessary. In addition some supermarket chains are going 'organic'. By this I mean they are taking only organically grown fruit and vegetables rather than the mass produced alternatives, artificially fertilized and sprayed with pesticides. In Britain the Safeway chain of stores (with 128 branches) stocks much organically grown produce and their spokesman has been reported as saying: 'Demand exceeds supply. The public want to buy the produce for the taste, health and environmental reasons.' Interestingly this supermarket group, also in response to consumer demand, removed all unnecessary additives from their produce and announced the fact at a special news conference in June 1985. The first products to be modified were those consumed by children, such as fish fingers, sausages, ice cream, jellies, soft drinks, etc.

With these results to their credit, Hyperactive Child Support Group members should be proud of their achievements. Despite the indifference of the medical profession, the group has a thriving membership, national and international recognition of their work and acceptance that hyperactivity is a real problem. However, doctors still consider the group to be full of misfits, extremists and health-food fanatics. They consider many of the group's ideas on the causes and management of hyperactivity to be wrong and often dangerous. There is more than a grain of truth in this belief. A void has existed (until recently) in the knowledge and understanding of the problem of hyperactivity. This void was soon filled by a disparate group of individuals each claiming to know the answers and pushing their own pet theories. Suggestions as to causes ranged from the sublime to the ridiculous and included vitamin deficiencies, trace metal deficiencies, metal poisoning, food allergy, aerosol allergy and even North Sea Gas allergy! Parents were urged to remove all chemicals from the house and garden, replace their gas cookers and aluminium pots and feed their children replacement vitamins and minerals. Such ideas have served only to reinforce the 'fringe medicine image' that doctors have of the group.

With so many members of the Hyperactive Child Support Group totally disillusioned with doctors and the doctors almost completely opposed to the group itself a state of mutual distrust and antagonism developed and still persists. This is most unfortunate as both have much to learn from each other. Ultimately it is the children who come off worst in this crossfire of mistrust. I would hope the Hyperactive Child Support Group will open up their meetings to more doctors and allow more critical evaluation of their management routines, and that doctors might also open their minds and investigate more closely the link between diet and overactive behaviour.

8

How Safe are
Processed Foods?*

Dietary factors in ill-health are becoming increasingly important. The link between the intake of saturated fats and heart disease has already been established, as has the connection between high blood pressure and salt consumption. At the other end of this ill-health spectrum are the more subtle problems that occur with certain foods. For example, milk and eggs are often involved in childhood eczema, and chocolate can bring on wheezing in asthmatics. A more contentious, but no less important, connection exists in the link between hyperactivity and certain food additives (i.e. the chemicals added during processing).

Parents who find their child's health and behaviour improving on a special diet often become suspicious of what goes into some manufactured foods and hanker after the days when organically grown produce was the norm rather than the exception. They may join the band of 'food watchers', people who question and examine very closely the foods we eat nowadays and how they are presented to us. Labels are scrutinized for ingredients, and fresh foods preferred in place of their prepacked rivals. The bland assurances from experts in the food industry are no longer accepted without challenge. In fact many of these people question the need for food processing at all, so it is as well to review the methods employed in food manufacturing.

It is reckoned that about 500,000 cows are required to provide the population of London with regular supplies of milk, cream, cheese and yoghurt. The cows need grass to feed on and

*Most of the details on nutrition and the processing of food contained in this chapter are taken directly from Prof. A. Stewart Truswell. *ABC of Nutrition*, British Medical Association, with the kind permission of author and publisher.

the grass is grown in the many acres of farmland in the South of England. About 3½ million acres of farmland are required to sustain the cows who keep the population of London in fresh dairy produce. Every day milk is collected from farms and transported to dairies where it is pasteurized, bottled and further distributed or processed. This complex distribution would be impossible (and the end product not fit for consumption) without some form of processing. The same applies to other foodstuffs such as fruit, meat and fish. So-called 'fresh' fruit often comes from half way across the world and has been in storage for weeks. Bananas, for example are picked in the tropics before they are ripe, shipped and stored at a controlled even temperature and ripened by exposure to ethylene gas (which is given off naturally by ripening fruit). Oranges are picked ripe, shipped and stored at a lower temperature in dry air with a raised carbon dioxide level. The skins are protected from mould infections by wrapping with chemically impregnated paper. Although these fruits have been in artificial environments, they are intact and alive and their cells are absorbing oxygen and producing carbon dioxide. In short, if you want a varied diet with a reasonable supply of fruit and vegetables all year round you cannot get around some form of artificial processing of the foods involved.

However, we may well be taking this processing of food too far. As much as 80 per cent of the food eaten in Western society is processed in one way or another. This is in stark contrast to our hunter-gatherer ancestors, 'hunter-gatherer' because they hunted meat and fish and gathered vegetables and fruit. Our ancestors were lean, ate more plant than animal foods, had a high fibre intake, took no salt or alcohol and sugar only in the form of wild honey.

Nowadays we are encouraged for health reasons to eat foods from the 'basic four' food groups: meat and alternates; fruit and vegetables; bread and cereals; and milk and milk products. Because no single food contains all essential nutrients we must select a variety of foods from these groups. For example, wheat lacks vitamins A, B_{12}, C and D and is very low in calcium, while beef contains little or no calcium, vitamins A, C or D or dietary fibre. On the other hand, wheat is an excellent source of fibre and beef of iron and vitamin B_{12}. The two together provide more nutrients than either alone, but between them have no vitamins C or D and hardly any calcium. The addition of citrus fruit or salad brings vitamin C into the mixture and milk or cheese adds the missing calcium and a little vitamin D. This is why we should choose from each of the four food groups. Each group has some deficiencies which the other three make up between them. We should aim to eat more than one serving each day from each group, not restricting ourselves to just one or two groups, nor indeed always eating the same food from a particular group. That way we minimize the possibility of deficiency in or excess of any particular nutrient. Some nutrients can be bad for health if taken in excess, for example, a high saturated fat diet raises the blood-fat levels and contributes to heart disease. Too much salt may cause blood pressure problems.

This leads us back to the need for processing of food. If we are to enjoy a nutritious, varied and healthy diet we have to accept some form of artificial interference along the journey to our dinner tables. Foods are processed for the following main reasons:

1. To preserve the food and extend the shelf-life. Preservation reduces wastage and hence cost. It enables us to eat our favourite foods all year round and so enables us to benefit from economies of scale by growing large quantities of food over large areas of suitable land.
2. Processing makes food safe by destroying dangerous organisms and toxins present.
3. Processing or preparation may improve the attractiveness of food, its flavour and its appearance.
4. Processing provides convenience and convenient foods relieve much of the drudgery associated with cooking.

There are several different methods of food preservation and processing. Among them are: drying, in order to produce concentrated forms of the food involved, for example milk powder; freezing; addition of salt and/or sugar; heating, for example, pasteurization; ionizing radiation, a new technique for sterilizing spices, etc; fermentation, which produces acid or alcohol (or both) in order to inhibit bacterial growth; separation; packaging, which prevents reinfection of food, once it has been heat-sterilized, by sealing it in a can or other container; and the addition of chemical preservatives, the so-called 'food additives', which are used for a variety of purposes. The following are the main types of chemical used in processing, and the reasons for their use:

Anti oxidants: These are used to prevent the slow oxidation of oils and fats and the development of rancidity.

Emulsifiers: These keep oil and aqueous phase together in sauces.

Humectants: These prevent foods from drying out.

Food acids: These are naturally occurring acids. They are used for flavour or for technical reasons, e.g. to make pectin set.

Preservatives: Salt, vinegar and sugar have been used for centuries and are still the most widely used preservatives today. Preservatives are permitted in specified foods up to a maximum concentration, for example nitrates in bacon/ham.

Free running agents: These prevent caking or sticking.

Thickeners: Examples of these are vegetables gums, cellulose or starch derivatives.

Nutritional supplements: A number of foods have added vitamins and minerals, for example breakfast cereals.

Colourings: About half the colouring agents used in processing are natural, such as beetroot red. There is a short list of permitted synthetic colourings — the azo dyes.

Flavourings: There are over 2000 flavouring substances permitted by EEC regulations to be added to foods. The names of these flavourings are not necessarily declared on labels and they are not included in the E codes. Flavour recipes are often trade secrets.

Miscellaneous: This category includes enzymes, bleaching agents, surfactants, firming agents, antifoaming agents, phosphates, air excluders and propellents for aerosol food containers.

Contaminants: Along the journey from farm to dinner table some unplanned additives can get into food, such as pesticides, drugs, heavy metals, industrial chemicals and other pollutants.

Because of the complex nature of the food industry a special committee exists to examine the many additives used in food processing and to test their safety. Britain had the first food safety legislation in the world (the Sale of Food and Drugs Act 1875, which was replaced in 1984 by the Food Act). A different committee of experts advises the Minister of Agriculture, Fisheries and Foods and the Department of Health. This is known as the Food Advisory Committee and it is in regular contact with the EEC Scientific Committee for Food, the joint FAO/WHO expert committee on food additives and food toxicologists around the world.

Before any additive is allowed to be used in foodstuffs it is tested in various animal species and then continuously kept under review by food toxicologists. Experts conclude that while the various components in our diet account for around 35 per cent of deaths from cancer, food additives account for 1 per cent. In other words we are more at risk from the other substances in food.

All of this should be very reassuring and allow us to sleep easily knowing that the foods we eat are passed as safe by the experts. However, recent reports suggest that these committees are not necessarily the guardians of health they are made out to be. The committees which deal with the safety of food additives are covered by the Official Secrets Act. Consequently any research into their activities and decisions is necessarily limited. Serious doubts have been expressed about the adequacy of safety testing procedures dealing with food additives. In addition a report by the London Food Commission in 1986 (dealing with pesticide residues in food) claims that tests carried out by the Ministry of Agriculture, Fisheries and Food are so inadequate that they would detect only 110 of the 426 pesticide residues currently permitted in agriculture. Concern about the long-term effects of pesticide exposure covers the possible causation of cancer, birth abnormalities, and genetic defects. There is also suspicion about the involvement of pesticide residues in food allergy, asthma and skin allergy. The London Food Commission report suggests that chemicals already in the environment can enhance the toxicity of pesticides (the 'cocktail effect') and the commission has found research linking at least 49 pesticides with cancer, 31 with birth defects, and 61 with genetic defects.

With these serious doubts being expressed about the food we eat and the 'experts' who oversee food processing it is not surprising that people turn more and more towards health food shops for their produce. Here, at least one would imagine we can be sure of the quality of the goods purchased. Surely they should be organically grown and free from unnecessary additives? However even these outlets are not free from commerical exploitation. A report from the United States has stated that many 'organically grown' products (as advertised in health food shops) are wrongly and dishonestly labelled. A British National Consumer Council report (*Which?* magazine) confirmed that British products do not live up to the claims made in the advertisements. Almost 50 per cent of samples of dried fruit had been treated with sulphur dioxide although most, contrary to law, did not state this on the label. Some 'natural' vitamin mixtures included synthetic derivatives. The stores stocked highly processed, coloured and flavoured and vitamin-enriched soya products — despite carrying banners denouncing such goods! In addition the health shops were more expensive than their supermarket rivals. The herbal and medicinal products sold in some of these establishments are also of dubious quality. A study of fever-few extracts sold as herbal tablets showed a remarkable variance in the amount of fever-few actually in the tablets compared with the label descriptions. In one case 200 times more fever-few was claimed than was actually present! In one homoeopathic fever-few product there was no detectable amount found at all!

These rather alarming reports make it difficult to know where to go for healthy uncontaminated and additive-free foods. My own feeling is that one should use (and trust) one's own common sense. Where at all possible, use fresh fruit and vegetables in preference to packaged or tinned alternatives. If such foods come from an organic source so much the better. (Don't go on a 50-mile drive just to get a bag of potatoes from a healthier source — you will only pollute the atmosphere with the unnecessary journey!) Ask your local greengrocer or supermarket manager to stock more fresh, organically grown foods, and keep up the pressure. Draw attention to the additives you are concerned about and let it be known how potentially harmful they are.

However, do keep a sense of perspective on the problem and try not to become extreme — there are very many people who prefer processed foods, whether they are harmful or not.

If you would like to learn more about nutrition and a detailed review of food manufacturing then I suggest that you read the following books:

Erik Millstone, *Food Additives. Taking the Lid Off What We Really Eat,* Penguin Books, price £2·95

Prof. A. Stewart Truswell, *ABC of Nutrition,* BMA Publications, BMA House, Tavistock Square, London WC1H 9JR, price £4·95

Conclusion

1. Hyperactivity in children is a real and very demanding problem for parents.
2. A considerable number of hyperactive children respond to a dietary change with a marked reduction in their over-active behaviour.
3. A logical, step-by-step approach as recommended in this book will guide you to a successful conclusion with your child.
4. If this approach does *not* work then be guided by the advice from those health professionals who deal with hyperactive children regularly.
5. As part of an overall review of your child's and family's diet try and avoid unnecessary food additives and cut back (or remove) very sweet produce and don't permit an over-indulgence in sweets, crisps, chocolates, fizzy drinks, etc. Do allow some treats, though!
6. Do not become a zealot and be wary of all extremists in the health food or allergy movements. The important messages that such people often carry are usually buried in a mixture of nonsense and half truths.
7. Keep a sense of perspective on these problems — not every child with an exuberant personality is hyperactive.

If this book has helped you in any way to manage your hyperactive child, then I am delighted. I am also very happy that at least one child will lead a happier life free from unnecessary medication and free also from heavy-handed psychological investigations.

Appendix 1

Glossary of Medical Terms

Additive: Food. One of the many substances used in food processing.

Allergy: Tissue sensitivity to certain substances.

Allergen: Any substance capable of producing an allergic reaction, for example pollen, which causes hay-fever.

Allergist: A doctor specializing in the management of allergic disorders.

Allergic Irritability Syndrome: A very descriptive term for a pattern of behaviour seen in some children with untreated allergies. Such children have mood swings, irritability and aggressive behaviour. They usually have very obvious features of allergy such as blocked nose, puffy eyes and repeated sneezing.

Allergic reaction: An abnormal response to a substance tolerated well by normal (i.e. non-allergic) individuals.

Allergy tests: Investigations to determine if someone is allergic and what exactly he or she is allergic to.

Amphetamines: Stimulant drugs used in the treatment of some forms of hyperactivity.

Artificial colourings/preservatives: Substances used in food processing to prolong shelf-life and make food stuffs look appetizing.

Asthma: A condition of the chest with features of cough, wheezing and shortness of breath. Occasionally the shortness of breath becomes extreme, when the situation is described as an asthma attack.

Barbiturates: Drugs used for a variety of reasons but principally as sedatives or hypnotics. Their use is severely restricted nowadays because of their potential for abuse. Barbiturates have no place in the treatment of hyperactivity.

Bronchitis: An inflammation of the lung tubes.

Child psychiatrist: A doctor specializing in the psychological problems of children.

Clinical psychologist: Not usually a medical doctor. Someone trained in psychology and psychological approaches to behaviour problems.

Conjunctivitis: An inflammation of the whites of the eyes.

Danders: A mixture of fur or hair, scale and urine shed from animals.

Dust: Small particles found on shelves, cupboards, etc., including what is picked up with the vacuum cleaner.

E Numbers: A coding system devised to substitute the specific names of some food additives with numbers, e.g. curcumin, which is designated E100.

Eczema: The descriptive term given to a skin condition characterized by redness, itch, blistering and weeping.

Educational psychologist: A psychologist interested in the problems children have with their educational needs.

Evening Primrose Oil: A polyunsaturated fatty acid which is useful in treating some children who are hyperactive.

Feingold Ben: A doctor from California who first proposed the theory linking hyperactivity to diet.

Glue ear: A condition where thick fluid accumulates in the inner ear and interferes with hearing.

Hay fever: A term used to describe the collection of symptoms of blocked, runny, itchy nose; red, itchy, watery eyes; and sneezing.

House dust mites: Microscopic insects which live in and feed off household dust. They are responsible for many different types of allergy.

Hyperactivity: A particular form of abnormal behaviour in children characterized by restlessness, mood swings, inattentiveness and irritability.

Inhaler: A spray aerosol containing medicine used in asthma management.

Migraine: A specific type of recurring headache often associated with visual disturbances, nausea and vomiting.

Minimal brain damage: A label implying brain damage so minute that it cannot be detected by sophisticated brain scans.

Moulds: Fungi which grow in old damp houses or moist aired conservatories, etc.

Oligo-antigenic diet: A very, very restricted diet containing only a few basic foods thought not to be involved in allergy.

Paediatrician: A doctor specializing in the health care of children.

Pollen: The fertilizing powder formed in flowers.

Psychotherapy: A form of therapy for psychological disorders where children are helped to understand their own difficulties. This may involve the whole family if it is felt that tensions within the family unit are creating problems.

Rhinitis: Inflammation of the lining of the nose with features such as an itchy, blocked, running nose and sneezing.

Salicylate (sodium salicylate or aspirin): A chemical which is widely used in drug treatments and easily manufactured for commercial use. It also occurs naturally in certain foods.

Theophylline: The group name for certain drugs in asthma treatments.

Appendix 2

Diagnostic Score Card for Allergic Irritability Syndrome

1 Does your child get one 'head cold' after another?　　　　　　　　　　　　　　YES/NO

2 Does your child have a constant blocked nose?　　　　　　　　　　　　　　　YES/NO

3 Does your child breathe constantly through his mouth?　　　　　　　　　　　YES/NO

4 Does your child sneeze a lot, especially first thing in the morning?　　　　　YES/NO

5 Does your child have dark circles around the eyes?　　　　　　　　　　　　YES/NO

6 Does your child have puffy eyes?　　　　　　YES/NO

7 Does your child repeatedly rub at his/her nose to relieve itch?　　　　　　　YES/NO

8 Does your child appear constantly irritable?　YES/NO

9 Does your child have difficulty in concentrating?　　　　　　　　　　　　　YES/NO

10 Does your child have bouts of disruptive behaviour for no obvious reason?　YES/NO

Score two points for each YES, none for each NO. A score of six points or more indicates that your child should be assessed for allergic rhinitis and considered to have Allergic Irritability Syndrome.

Appendix 3

Diagnostic Score Card for Asthma

1 Does your child have a persisting or recurring cough? YES/NO
2 Does your child cough with physical effort? YES/NO
3 Does your child wheeze often? YES/NO
4 Does your child wheeze or get short of breath with physical exercise? YES/NO
5 Does your child wheeze with every head cold? YES/NO
6 Does your child miss a lot of school because of chest problems? YES/NO
7 Does your child get a lot of 'bronchitis' or 'wheezy bronchitis'? YES/NO
8 Has your child frequently been described as 'bronchial', 'chesty'? YES/NO
9 Does your child get episodes of sudden shortness of breath? YES/NO
10 Is there a family history of asthma, eczema or hay fever? YES/NO

Score two points for each YES, none for each NO. A score of four points or more indicates that your child almost certainly has asthma and should be assessed for this condition.

Appendix 4

Progress Score Card for Teachers

Hyperactivity in Children

Answer YES if the following describe the pupil:

1	Makes disruptive noises (Humming, rattling, etc.)	YES/NO
2	Wanders around the classroom	YES/NO
3	Disturbs other children	YES/NO
4	Speaks out of turn	YES/NO
5	Short attention span	YES/NO
6	Ignores teacher's instructions	YES/NO
7	Belligerent	YES/NO
8	Constantly 'on the go'	YES/NO
9	Poor academic performance	YES/NO
10	Talks incessantly	YES/NO

Score 2 points for each YES answer and record the total score at the beginning of the management routine. Repeat the questionnaire at six-weekly intervals. Allow at least three months before assessing full impact of the management routine. A drop in score of at least 50 per cent should be considered encouraging enough to continue with the programme.

Appendix 5

Artificial Colourings and Preservatives Involved in Hyperactivity

There is a wide range of chemicals used in food processing some of which can cause allergic reactions in susceptible children. The main chemicals added (called 'additives') are emulsifiers, thickeners, colour dyes, preservatives, spices, enzymes and bacterial inhibitors. These additives are included by the manufacturers for a variety of reasons, such as to make the products look attractive, to enhance the taste or just to extend the shelf-life.

It is impossible to know for certain which of these chemicals produce allergic responses in children and why they occur at all. However, we now know that children with allergies should avoid the more notorious food additives which have caused problems to others in the past.

The complete list of additives is quite long and new chemicals are included quite frequently. For those readers who may wish to look at this topic in more detail I recommend *Look at the Label*, a publication by the Ministry of Agriculture, Fisheries and Food which explains what the labels on prepacked food mean, and why they are important. Copies of the booklet are available, free of charge, from Her Majesty's Stationery Office, P.O. Box 569, London SE1 9NH. When ordering remember to ask for any amendments. Your local library may be able to give you a copy.

In brief, the labels on foodstuffs should include a complete list of ingredients, including additives. Each additive is usually listed by the category name which explains its function in the food. Quite often the exact name will be replaced by the serial number given to the additive (the 'E' number), for example, 'preservative — E200' or 'flavour enhancer — monosodium glutamate'.

If you have a child with allergies — particularly if the child is troubled by asthma, eczema or hyperactivity — then look carefully at the labels on packaged foods for the list of additives. Where practical, use fresh rather than prepacked foods and avoid the following, notorious additives:

E102 Tartrazine
E110 Sunset Yellow
E124 Ponceau 4R
E127 Erythrosine
E150 Caramel
E210–219 Benzoates and benzoic acid
E320 Butylated hydroxyanisole (BHA)
E321 Butylated hydroxytoluene (BHT)

For a fuller list of additives which may cause problems see pages 36–7.

As an example, foods likely to contain tartrazine include:

Fruit squash and cordial
Coloured fizzy drinks
Pickles
Bottled sauces
Salad cream
Cakes (shop bought)
Soups (packets and tins)
Custard
Filled Chocolates
Instant puddings
Coloured sweets
Jelly
Ice Cream
Jam and lollies
marmalade
Curry powder
Yoghurt
Mustard

Tartrazine is water soluble and gives a pleasant lemon yellow colour to foods. It is also used in some medicine capsules. Incidence of sensitivity is between 1 in 10,000 and 1 in 1000.

Do remember: A label stating 'permitted colourings and flavourings' may still contain one of these troublesome additives. Where at all practical make sure you are aware of what your child eats and drinks.

Alternative Methods of Diagnosing and Treating Allergies in Children

Doubtful Value Tests

Pulse Testing: This relies on the measurement of a rise in pulse after consuming something likely to cause an allergic reaction. This is open to so many variables that in practical terms it is useless.

Basophil/Degranulation Test: A test-tube diagnosis for allergies. In this test blood cells (called basophils) break up when exposed to allergens to which they are sensitive. This can be observed with a microscope.

Sublingual Drop Tests: Diluted solution of foods to be tested are put under the tongue and the patient observed for allergic reactions. A very, very imperfect test and in practical terms of no use.

Cytotoxic Testing: A diagnosis of allergy is suggested if a food solution is added to a blood sample and the white cells are observed to die. This test is time-consuming, gives false positives and is considered inaccurate so often as to be useless in diagnosis.

Intra-dermal Testing: A deeper form of skin-prick testing, this carries a small risk of producing a severe allergic reaction. There are too many false positives with this test for it to be considered useful in diagnosis.

Useless Tests

Hair Analysis: This involves a hair sample analysed by a private laboratory. This will not detect any form of allergy and also produces widely differing results (even from the same head!) when testing for trace metal deficiencies.

Radionics, Radiesthesia, Psionic Medicine and Dowsing: Apparently these are forms of extra sensory perception. They are useless in diagnosing or treating children's allergies.

Dangerous Advice and Practices

Occasionally, children are subjected to various diets and other forms of treatment by their parents which are likely to cause harm. Almost exclusively this involves children with allergic problems.

These are the most frequently encountered nowadays:

Auto-immune Urine Therapy: In other words the child is made to drink his/her own urine. This, apparently, is a homoeopathic remedy. Apart from the obvious unpleasantness involved, this practice is potentially dangerous.

Macrobiotic Diets: These are likely to produce nutritional deficiencies in growing children.

Supplementation of Diet with Trace Elements: Allergies cannot be cured by vitamin or trace element supplementation. The overuse of vitamin and trace mineral preparations can actually cause problems in children.

Intestinal Candidiasis: The theory here is that the intestinal tract has been 'taken over' by the growth of an organism called *candida albicans* (also known as yeast or thrush). Treatment involves low-sugar, low-yeast diets and a powder to kill off the *candida* in the bowel. Such suggestions and treatments are useless and only deflect attention away from correct procedures.

Useful Addresses

United Kingdom

Association for Children with Learning Difficulties, Quirral House, Pitch Place, Thursley, Godalming, Surrey

Hyperactive Children's Support Group, c/o Sally Bunday, 71 Whyke Lane, Chichester, West Sussex, PO19 2LD.

Ireland

Hyperactive Child Support Group, c/o Sarah Nichols, 4 Elton Park, Sandycove, Co. Dublin.

Australia

Hyperactivity Association of NSW, 24/29 Bertram Street, Chatswood, NSW 2067

Hyperactivity Association of South Australia Inc, 18 King William Road, North Adelaide, South Australia 5006

Hyperactive Help (WA), 88 Manning Street, Scarborough, WA 6019

Launceston Hyperactivity Association, Mrs P. Motton, c/o P.O., Meander, Tasmania 7304

New Zealand

Auckland Hyperactivity Association Inc, P.O. Box 36–099, Northcote, Auckland

Waikato Hyperkinetic Children's Support Group, c/o 10 McFarlane Street, Hamilton

Wellington Hyperactivity and Allergy Association Inc, 93 Waipapa Road, Hataitai, Wellington

Index

77